CONTENTS

INTRODUCTION & INSTRUCTIONS

· ·

{Or, "Why Should I Give Other People Awards When
I Rarely Receive the Adulation I So Richly Deserve?"}

· ·

Most people don't get all the praise they deserve. And no one gets as much as they crave.

Of course, most of us don't *give* enough praise, either. This is not good. Praising others is a surefire way to feel great yourself. Researchers at the University of Pennsylvania tested the effects of several positive psychology techniques, including writing thank-you letters to people who had never been properly recognized for their kindness. As described in the *Harvard Mental Health Letter*, "Participants immediately exhibited a huge increase in happiness scores. This impact was greater than that from any other intervention, with benefits lasting for a month." And depending on the people they were writing to, who knows what it may have done for their careers?

For your own sake, resolve today to start lavishing others with positive vibes, panegyrics, gratitude, and good-natured ribbing. This book makes it painless, and virtually effortless. Don't be ashamed of your shallow intentions. The people who receive your awards won't have any idea how little thought and time you put into this. They will simply be dazzled and delighted. You will feel like a benevolent god. Win-win. (Note: in case you know a lot of flakes, we've conveniently created awards for all sorts of "achievements"—including procrastination, gossip, and mediocre parenting—so no one will be left out.)

Utilize this book with abandon. Cross out words you don't like, and rewrite as you wish. Don't overthink things when choosing to give an award—just personalize, punch out, and present. Give them to coworkers, friends, frenemies, roomies, relatives, crushes, and lovers. Offer them on appropriate occasions, or out of the blue. Then watch as your happiness temperature rapidly becomes a feel-good fever.

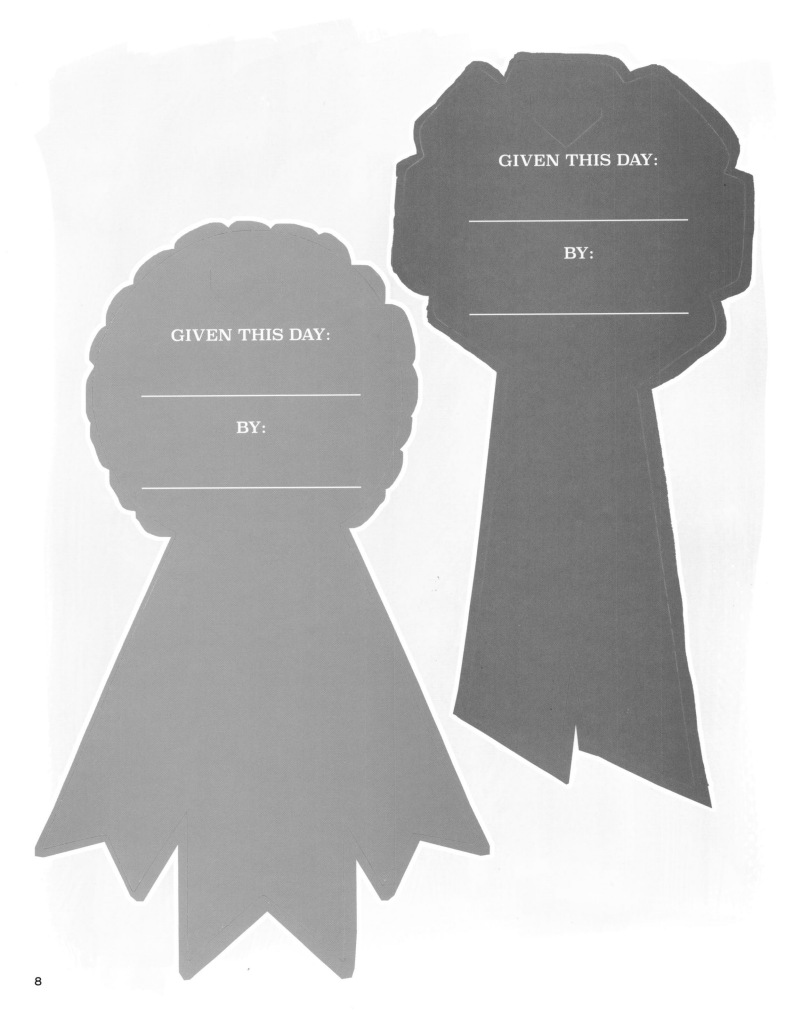

GIVEN THIS DAY:

_____

BY:

GIVEN THIS DAY:

_____

BY:

_____

8

DATE: _____

TO: _____

FROM: _____

GIVEN ON BEHALF OF THE
INTERNATIONAL MINISTRY
OF MISCHIEF AND CAPERS

GIVEN THIS DAY: _____

TO: _____

BY: _____

TO: _____

FROM: _____

DATE: _____

TO: _____

FROM: _____

DATE: _____

GIVEN ON THIS DAY:

_____

TO: _____

BY: _____

GIVEN THIS DAY:

_____

BY:

_____

14

15

GIVEN ON THIS DAY:

_____

TO: _____

BY: _____

GIVEN ON THIS DAY:

_____

TO: _____

BY: _____

ACHIEVEMENT
AWARD

For Outstanding Achievement
in Achieving an Achievement
You Wanted to Achieve

YOU DID IT. YOU REALLY DID IT.

OFFICIAL
GREAT LISTENER
and
DARN GOOD
ADVICE GIVER

BIG SHOULDERS
·
BIG HEART
·
BIG EARS

(METAPHORICALLY SPEAKING)

GIVEN ON THIS DAY:

_____

TO: _____

BY: _____

GIVEN IN GRATITUDE TO:

_____

BY: _____

DATE: _____

18

EXEMPLARY LEADERSHIP IN SETTING A TERRIBLE EXAMPLE

Bad Influence AWARD

DIDN'T KILL THE KID. TODAY.

ADEQUATE PARENTING AWARD
FOR EMINENT ACHIEVEMENT IN KINDA-OK CAREGIVING

FILL IN LIKE SO:

EXEMPLARY LEADERSHIP IN SETTING A TERRIBLE EXAMPLE

Bad Influence AWARD *Jamie*

STRENGTH · SPORTSMANSHIP ALMOST ZERO 'ROID RAGE

FITNESS SUPERSTAR

To: _____
From: _____
Date: _____

Given this day: _____

By: _____

"GOOD ENOUGH"
IS GREAT

FEELS SO
RIGHT

BEING SO
WRONG

To: _____
From: _____
Date: _____

WE ARE THE
CHAMPIONS,
MY FRIEND

20

MEDAL OF OUTSTANDING
PROFESSIONAL ACHIEVEMENT

TOTALLY
**KILLIN' IT
AT WORK**

Awarded to

_____

EXCELLENCE IN THE FIELD OF
KINDNESS & GENEROSITY

♡

WORLD'S
BIGGEST
(+ *Beautifulest*)
HEART

♡

BOW DOWN, Y'ALL

OFFICIAL
Master
of the
Universe

21

Given in gratitude by: _____

Date: _____

Given this day: _____

By: _____

FILL IN
LIKE SO:

Given in gratitude to: _____
Date: _____

Craig

_____

NAILED IT.

Granted to: _____

By: _____ Date: _____

YOU
HAVE
THE
POWER.

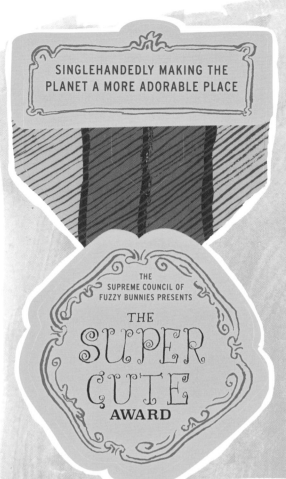

SINGLEHANDEDLY MAKING THE PLANET A MORE ADORABLE PLACE

THE
SUPREME COUNCIL OF
FUZZY BUNNIES PRESENTS

THE
SUPER
CUTE
AWARD

SUPREME JUDGMENT AND SPOT-ON INSTINCTS

BEST DECISION EVER

LEADERSHIP IN THE FIELD OF BEING ELEGANTLY WASTED

CLASSY
Drunk
AWARD

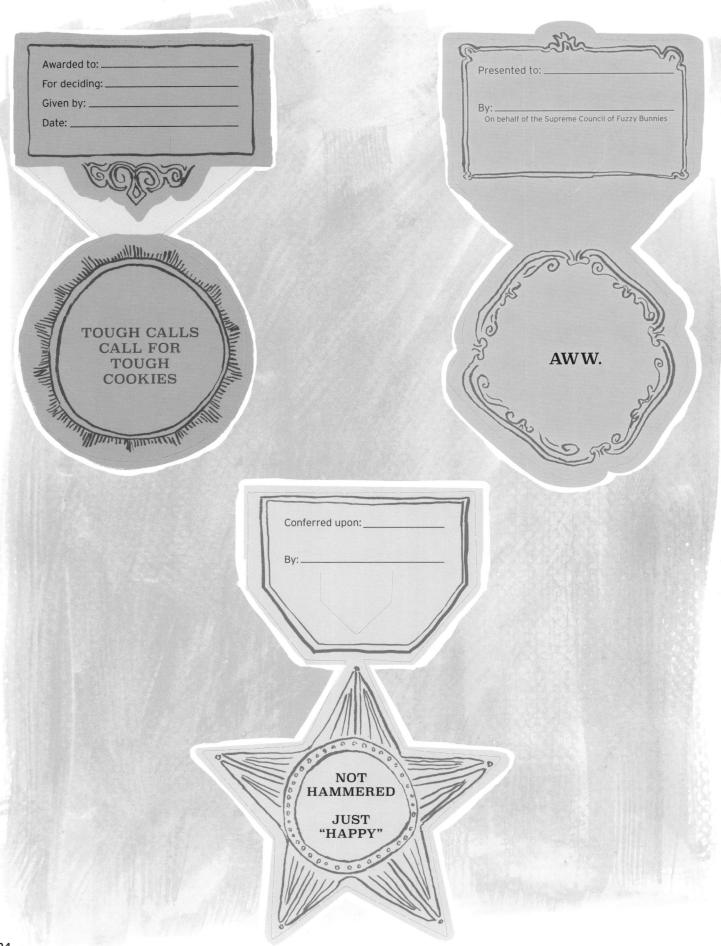

Awarded to: _____
For deciding: _____
Given by: _____
Date: _____

TOUGH CALLS
CALL FOR
TOUGH
COOKIES

Presented to: _____

By: _____
On behalf of the Supreme Council of Fuzzy Bunnies

AWW.

Conferred upon: _____

By: _____

NOT
HAMMERED

JUST
"HAPPY"

Consistently
SPILLING STUFF
Merit Badge

OFFICIAL
Gossip
MERIT BADGE

OFFICIAL
HIPSTER
MERIT BADGE

"I'M NOT A HIPSTER"

OFFICIAL
PLANT MURDERER
MERIT BADGE

OFFICIAL
Crazy Boss
SURVIVOR
MERIT BADGE

OFFICIAL
GREAT *Hair*
MERIT BADGE

25

FOLD TAB OVER AND HANG FROM COLLAR OR POCKET.

SPREADING RUMORS

Awarded to: _____

By: _____

Date: _____

TALKIN' SMACK

Awarded to: _____

By: _____

Date: _____

"OOPS, I DID IT AGAIN."

Awarded to: _____

By: _____

Date: _____

"STOP ME BEFORE I KILL AGAIN"

Awarded to: _____

By: _____

Date: _____

SO HIP IT HURTS

Awarded to: _____

By: _____

Date: _____

FOR OUTSTANDING PERFORMANCE BY A SCALP

Awarded to: _____

By: _____

Date: _____

"VENGEANCE SHALL BE MINE"

SELFIE-OBSESSED
MERIT BADGE

CONSTANTLY MISPLACED
Keys/Phone/Wallet
MERIT BADGE

OFFICIAL
NERD
MERIT BADGE

WORLD-CLASS
CHRONICALLY DISSATISFIED
COMPLAINER
MERIT BADGE

COMPULSIVE
Online
Shopping
MERIT BADGE

ACTUALLY
PRETTY
COOL
Parent
MERIT BADGE

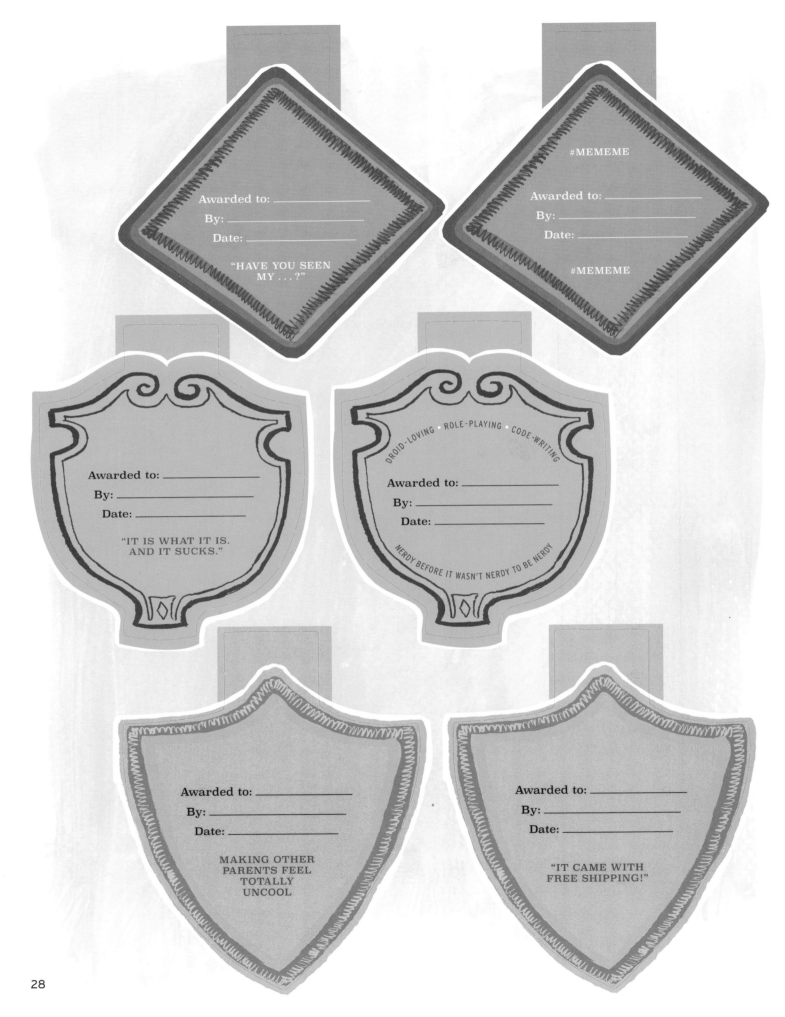

#MEMEME

Awarded to: _____

By: _____

Date: _____

#MEMEME

Awarded to: _____

By: _____

Date: _____

"HAVE YOU SEEN MY . . . ?"

Awarded to: _____

By: _____

Date: _____

"IT IS WHAT IT IS. AND IT SUCKS."

DROID-LOVING • ROLE-PLAYING • CODE-WRITING

Awarded to: _____

By: _____

Date: _____

NERDY BEFORE IT WASN'T NERDY TO BE NERDY

Awarded to: _____

By: _____

Date: _____

MAKING OTHER PARENTS FEEL TOTALLY UNCOOL

Awarded to: _____

By: _____

Date: _____

"IT CAME WITH FREE SHIPPING!"

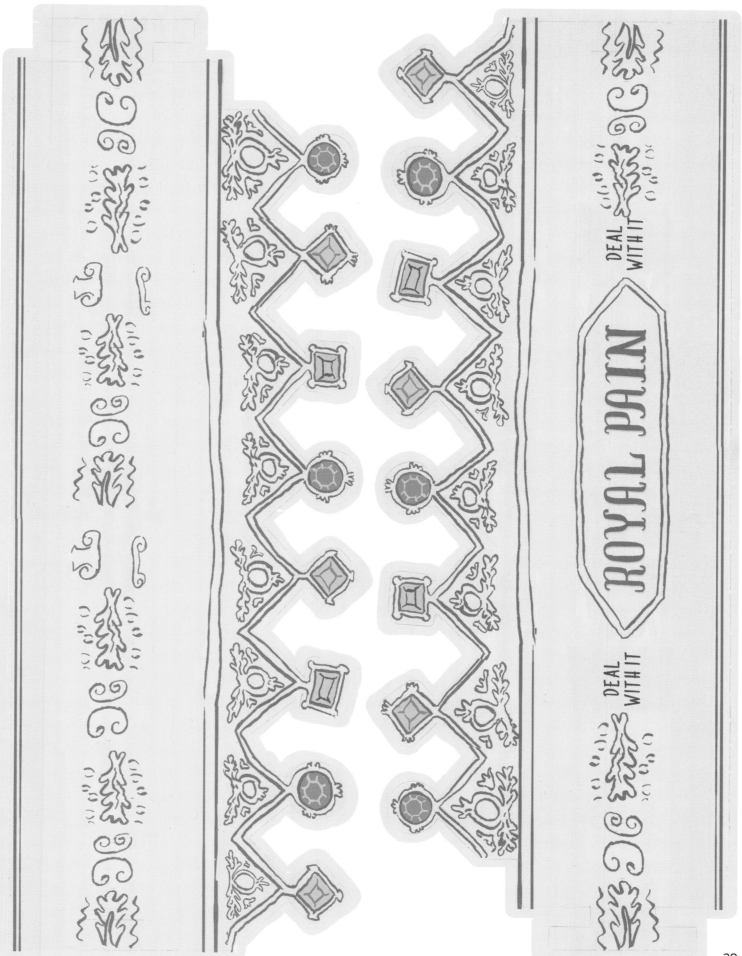

ROYAL PAIN

DEAL WITH IT

DEAL WITH IT

PUNCH OUT CROWN. FOLD IN SIDES OF TABS, INSERT INTO SLOTS, AND UNFOLD TABS TO SECURE.

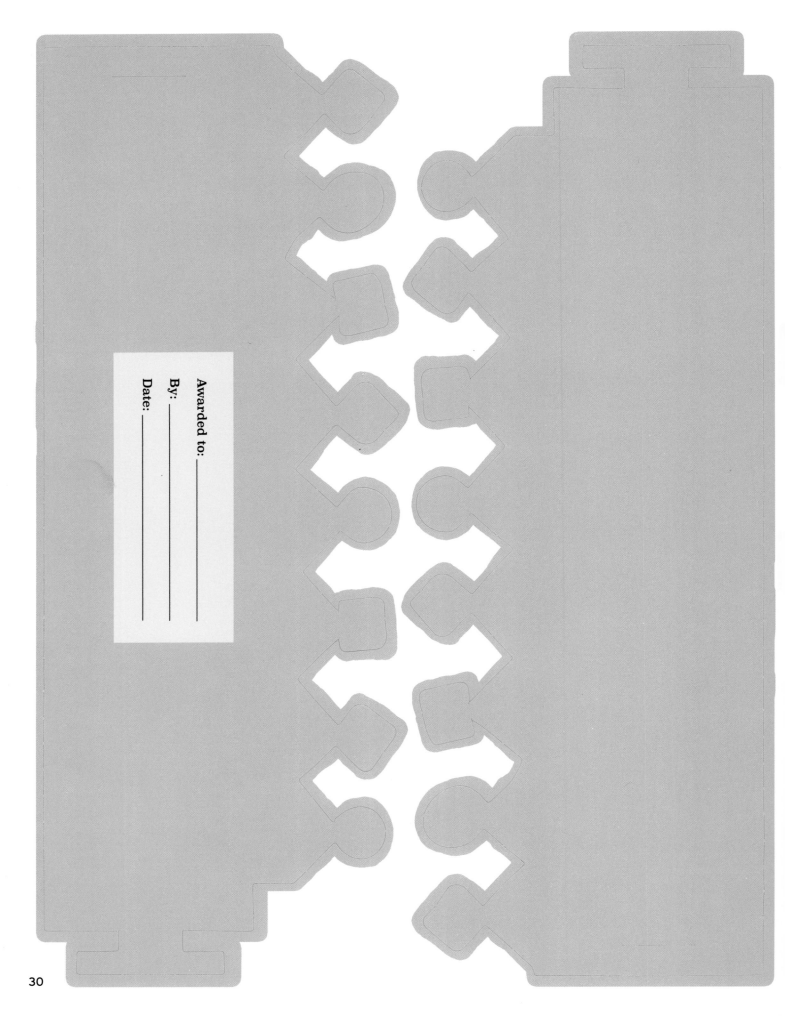

Awarded to:_____

By:_____

Date:_____

30

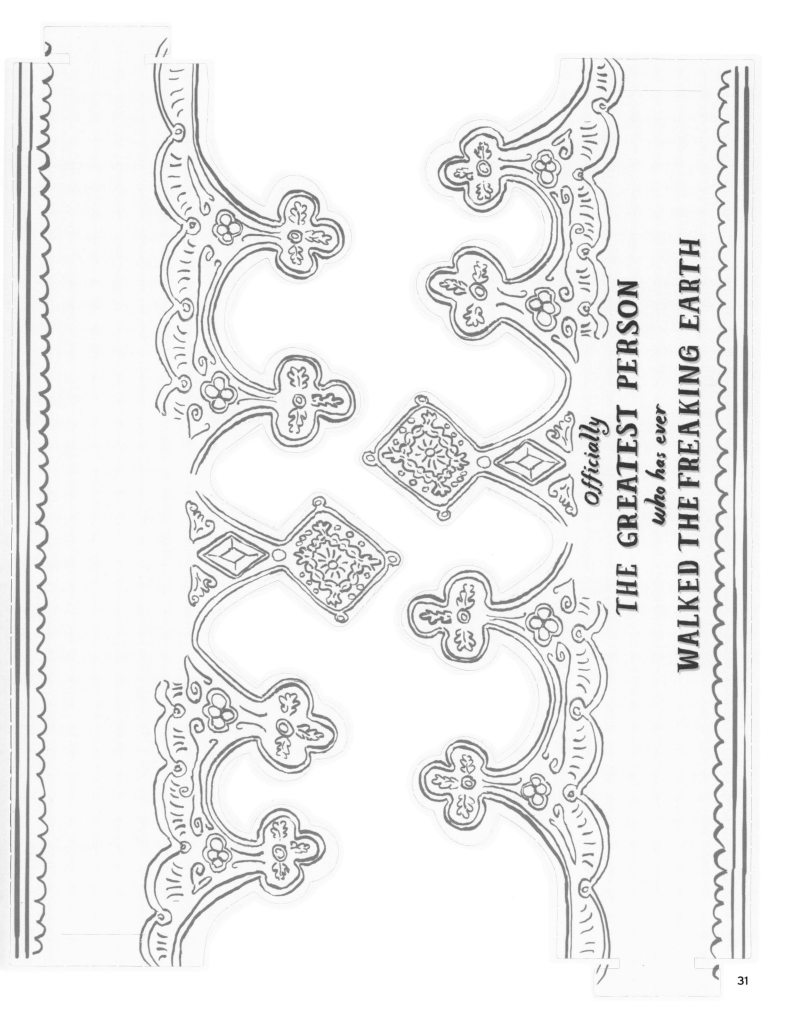

Officially
THE GREATEST PERSON
who has ever
WALKED THE FREAKING EARTH

Awarded to: _____

By: _____

Date: _____

32

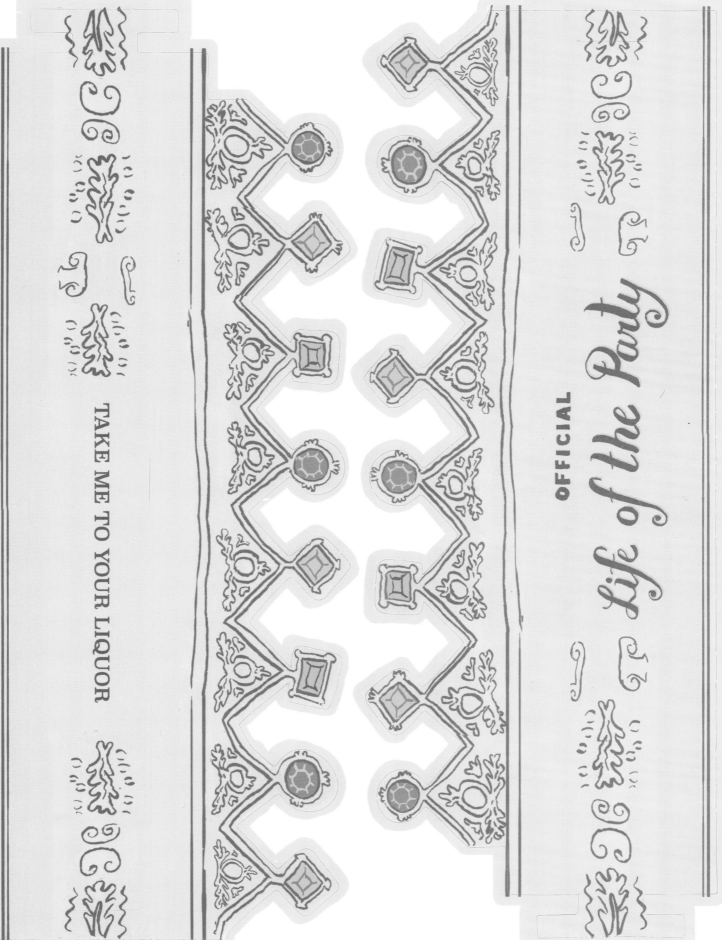

TAKE ME TO YOUR LIQUOR

OFFICIAL

Life of the Party

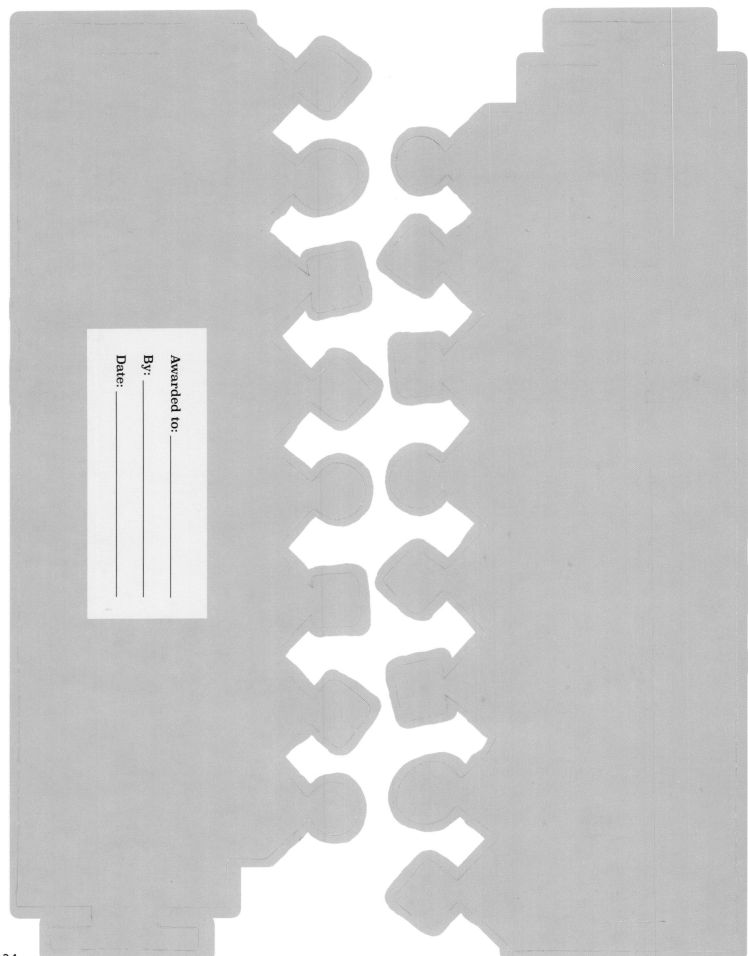

Awarded to: _____

By: _____

Date: _____

LET ME EAT CAKE

BIRTHDAY QUEEN

Given to the Birthday Queen:

By her royal subject(s):

Date:

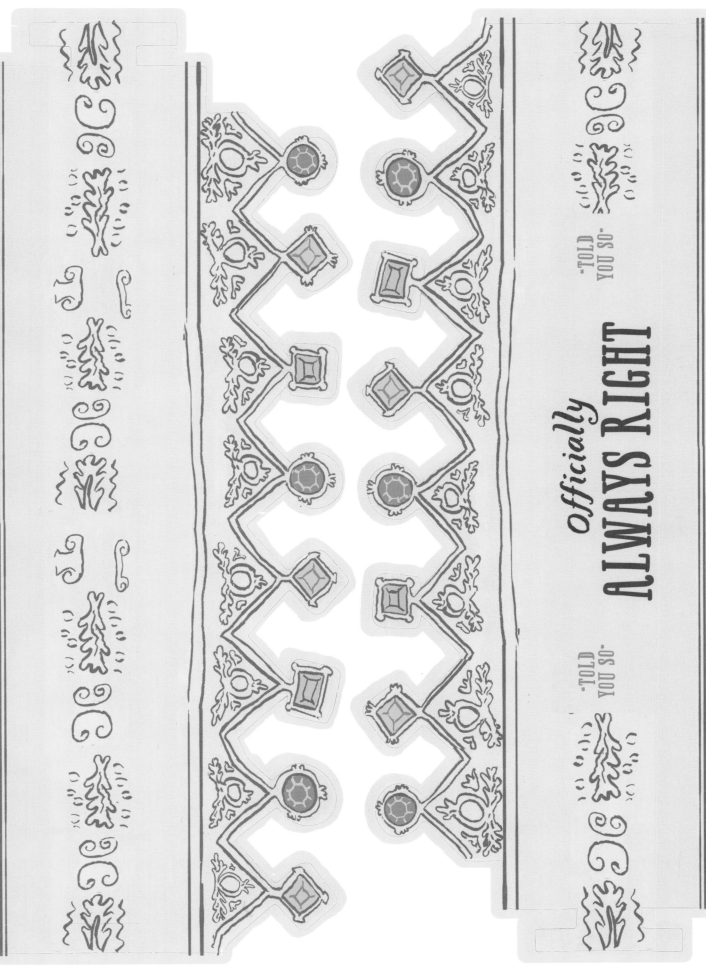

officially
ALWAYS RIGHT

-TOLD
YOU SO-

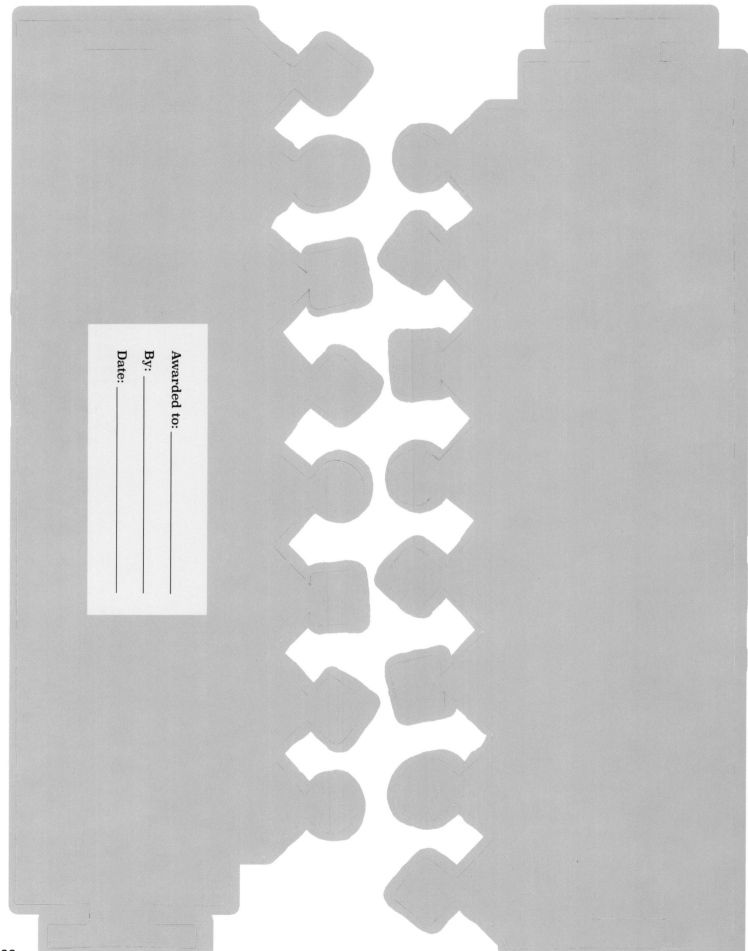

Awarded to:_____

By:_____

Date:_____

38

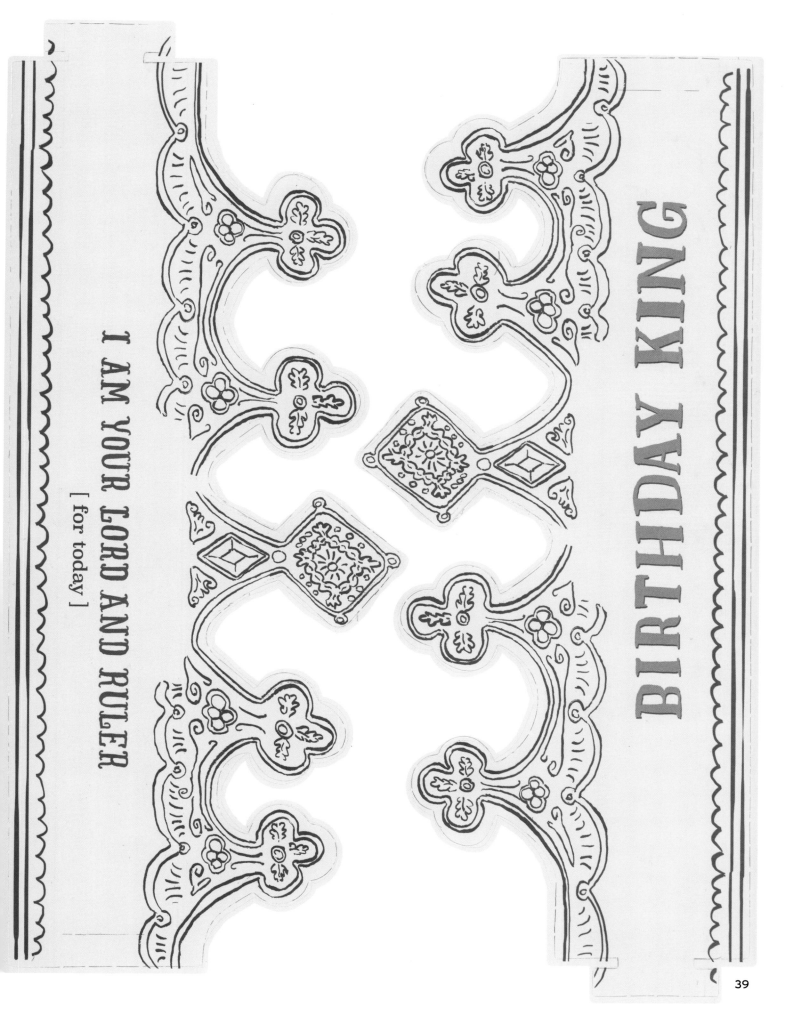

I AM YOUR LORD AND RULER

[for today]

BIRTHDAY KING

Given to the Birthday King:

By his royal subject(s): _____

Date: _____

40

TO ALL PERSONS LET IT BE KNOWN

THE GLOBAL CONSORTIUM of NE'ER-DO-WELLS & MISANTHROPES

HEREBY RECOGNIZES

AS AN OFFICIAL

EVIL GENIUS

AND GRANTS ALL PERTAINING RIGHTS & PRIVILEGES
AS WELL AS SEVERAL OTHER, NON-PERTAINING PRIVILEGES JUST FOR FUN
BECAUSE WE ARE EVIL AND WE CAN

THE SUPERIOR ALLIANCE of TOTAL KNOW-IT-ALLS

IN ASSOCIATION WITH

THE SECRET SOCIETY of SMARTER, BETTER PEOPLE

HEREBY RECOGNIZES

....

AS A

Cultural Snob

WITH ALL THE RIGHTS, PRIVILEGES, AND HONORS THERETO PERTAINING

Given this day: ....   Signed by: ....

WHEREAS We Have a Really Good Time and

WHEREAS You're Generally Sane and

WHEREAS I'm Glad We Moved In Together

BY THE POWER VESTED IN ME I DO HEREBY CONFER UPON

THE OFFICIAL TITLE OF

TOTALLY

Non-Crappy Cohabitator

Given this day: ....

Signed by: ....